D0549581

Magic

by Helen Orme

Trailblazers

Magic
by Helen Orme
Educational consultant: Helen Bird

Illustrated by Mik Brown

Published by Ransom Publishing Ltd.
51 Southgate Street, Winchester, Hants. SO23 9EH
www.ransom.co.uk

ISBN   978 184167 802 3

First published in 2009

Every effort has been made to locate all copyright holders of material used in this book. If any errors or omissions have occurred, corrections will be made in future editions of this book.

A CIP catalogue record of this book is available from the British Library.

Magic

Contents

Get the facts   5

Good luck, bad luck   6

Can famous magicians do real magic?   8

Mind reading   10

Witches and wizards   12

Houdini   14

Some handy spells   16

Fiction

The Disappearance   19

Magic word check   36

Magic

Get the facts

Good luck, bad luck

Is **walking under a ladder** bad luck?

It might be if something falls on your head!

Do you have something special, like a **mascot**, to bring good luck when you are watching your favourite football team or doing an exam?

Mascots and **good luck charms** have been around for thousands of years.

FRIDAY 13th

Some people have lucky numbers. **Thirteen** is thought to be an unlucky number.

Black cats are often thought to be lucky – but not always. Some people think it is bad luck if one runs across your path.

6

Some high-rise buildings don't have a thirteenth floor.

People who **hunt food** used to have magical ways of making sure that the hunting was good. **Cave paintings** of animals, dating back thousands of years, may have been painted to bring good luck to the hunters.

How about bringing bad luck to people?

The **Romans** brought bad luck to their enemies in a special way. They wrote a **message to the gods** on a piece of metal, asking them to do something **horrible** to the person they didn't like.

This **Roman curse** was found in Gloucestershire, England.

Honoratus to the holy god Mercury. I complain to your divinity that I have lost two wheels and four cows and many small belongings from my house.

I would ask you that you do not allow health to the person who has done me wrong, nor allow him to lie or sit or drink or eat, whether he is man or woman, whether boy or girl, whether slave or free, unless he brings my property to me.

But is any of this magic true?

You decide!

3

Can famous magicians do real magic?

?

Can they **cut a lady in half** and put her back together again?

Can they make a **bridge disappear**?

The magician **Franz Harary** made a video showing **Tower Bridge** vanishing.

Later, he explained how it was done. It's quite easy when you can make things vanish using a computer!

Now you see it ... Now you don't!

Another magician, **David Copperfield**, made the **Statue of Liberty** disappear.

He hasn't explained how he did it!

These are **great tricks** – but they are just tricks, not real magic!

Stage magicians use **special equipment** to help fool people.

Mirrors are important for these tricks. So are **secret compartments** where stage magicians can keep things hidden.

How to cut someone in half

The **magician** asks his **helper** to climb into a box. Then he closes the box and starts to **saw** through the middle.

The helper is **quite safe** because she is curled up in half of the box. She can **wave** to the audience and **waggle** her **feet** – even though she is being cut in half!

In fact there is a **second helper**, hidden below the box. The audience see the first helper's head and the (hidden) second helper's feet.

At the end of the trick the first helper can step out of the box – safe and well.

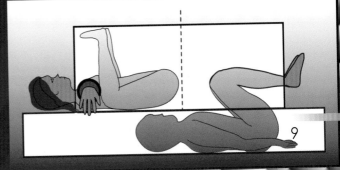

9

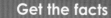
Mind reading

Is mind reading **magic**? No. It's just a **trick**.

Let me show you how to **read minds**!

First you need an **audience** and a **helper**. Agree on a code word with your helper, such as '**big**'.

Tell the audience you can read their minds.

Ask one member of the audience to choose an **object** in the room and tell your helper what it is.

Tell them to make sure you don't hear what it is.

Witches and wizards

Are there really witches and wizards?

In the **sixteenth** and **seventeenth** **centuries** most people in Europe believed in them. Some people thought that they were witches themselves.

Sometimes witches were blamed for a **bad harvest** or **sickness**. Harmless people could be **hanged** or even **burned to death** because people thought they were witches.

In **1612**, in **Lancaster**, England, ten men and women were hanged for **witchcraft**.

They were accused of murdering seventeen people by witchcraft.

One of the witches, called **Demdike**, described how they killed their victims.

'First make a model of clay. Then burn the model in a fire, or crumble it to dust. As the model is destroyed the victim will become ill, and die.'

Many **cultures** have people who say they have magic powers.

These are called **shamans**.

Many people believe that a shaman can **solve problems** for them, such as illness.

A shaman from the Oroqen people, in Siberia.

Does it work?

Sometimes. Scientists think that if you really believe that something will cure you, you will often get better.

The shamen would say that it is their powers that have made the difference.

YOU DECIDE WHICH IS RIGHT ...

Houdini

Harry Houdini was born in 1874. He was one of the **greatest magicians** that have ever lived.

Houdini is best known for his **escape tricks**.

In 1904 he was locked into the world's most **escape-proof handcuffs**. They had taken five years to make.

> It took Harry just over an hour to escape from them.

This is Harry being lowered into the **Chinese Water Torture** cell.

His feet were **locked** into a metal frame. He was lowered head first into the **tank of water**. The tank was hidden behind a curtain ...

A few minutes later, Houdini had **escaped**!

How did he do it?

No one knows!

Another trick was called the **Overboard Box**.

Harry was locked into **handcuffs** and **leg-irons**. He was put in a crate and nailed in.

The crate was thrown into a river.

Harry could **escape** from the crate in **under a minute**!

Harry Houdini **died** in **1926**. This is a picture of his grave.

Is he still there – or has he escaped?

15

Some handy spells

Problems with witches? Try a **witch bottle**!

These bottles contained all sorts of **horrible things**, such as **nails**, **human hair** and **urine**.

So how did they work?

If you buried one close to the front door, **witches** couldn't get into your house.

If you had one buried in your garden, it would cause **pain** to anyone trying to put a **curse** on any member of your family.

If someone was already cursed, you could throw the witch bottle on the fire. This would cause the witch a lot of pain until the curse was lifted. It might even kill the witch!

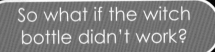

So what if the witch bottle didn't work?

You could try a **hag stone!**

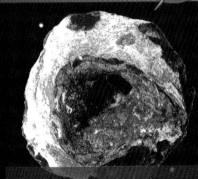

Hag stones are stones with a **hole** through them. They were believed to **protect people** from **witches.**

Which one is a hag stone, and which one a bagel?

A hag stone in the **stable** would stop the witch **stealing** your **horse.** At night, hag stones were hung by the bed to stop witches, demons or other evil creatures.

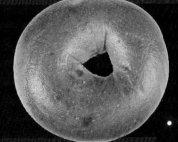

Help!
My house is full of rats and mice!

The bodies of **dried-up cats** have been found hidden in walls and roofs.

Sometimes a **favourite pet** would be **buried** inside the house. It was thought that the **spirit** of the cat would protect the house from rats.

Sometimes **mummified rats** are found with the cats.

17

Chapter 1:
The Theatre of Magic

'Don't worry, it's quite safe!'

Emma had never worked for a magician before. The Great Calosto had advertised on the Internet for a new assistant. Emma wondered why Daisy, the last assistant, had left so suddenly.

'This is the disappearing trick. When I shut the door of the cabinet, you go out through the back door.

'Make sure you are out before I push the sword through the cabinet! No one will see you – you will have disappeared. It's all done by mirrors!'

Emma had never worked for a magician before ...
Make sure you go out through the back door before I push the sword through!

The Theatre of Magic first opened two hundred years ago.

The greatest magicians in history had worked there. Some people said the theatre itself was magical.

It was Emma's first performance. She stepped into the cabinet and Calosto shut the door.

Quickly, Emma pressed the secret switch that opened the back door, and stepped out.

The Theatre of Magic opened two hundred years ago. Some people thought it was really magical!

Quickly, Emma opened the secret back door ...

Chapter 2:
A thrust to the heart

Back on the stage, Calosto showed the audience the sharp sword. He got ready to push it through the small hole in the front of the cabinet.

If anyone was in the box, it would go right through their heart.

A drum rolled. Calosto thrust the sword in. There was a terrible scream from the cabinet, and blood began oozing from under the door ...

But whose blood was it?

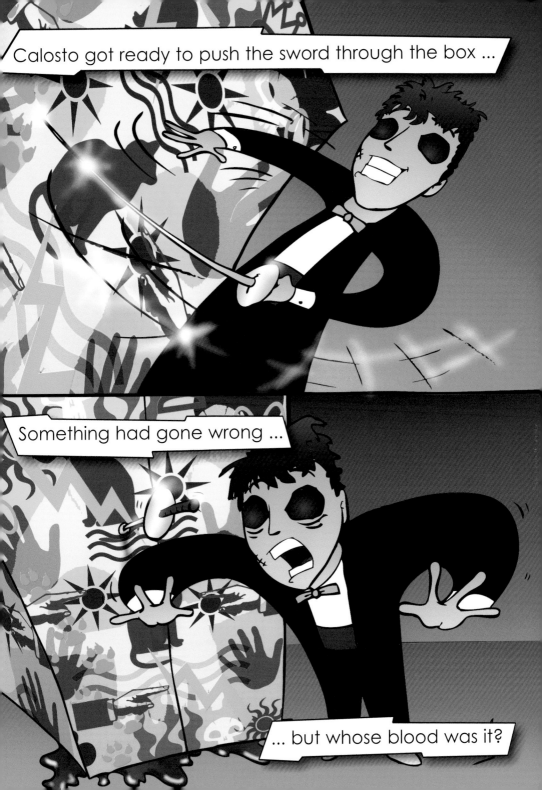

Emma found herself in a gloomy passage lit by burning torches. It was damp and a rotting smell filled the air.

The passage stretched away into the distance, and all along it there were iron doors. A terrible groaning came from some of them.

Emma looked through the nearest door – a bleak prison cell. There was someone inside. Emma knew who it was – Daisy, Calosto's last assistant!

'Quick!' Daisy whispered. 'There's a key hanging outside! Let me out!'

Chapter 3:
The old man

Quickly, Emma opened the door. Straight away, Daisy grabbed her and threw her into the cell. She locked the door.

'I'm going back, not you!' she said.

Then they heard footsteps, shuffling down the passage.

In fear, Daisy rushed to the back door of the cabinet. She opened it and went in – too soon! Calosto was just pushing the sword into the front door ...

The footsteps came closer.

Emma looked out through the bars. She saw a strange, ancient figure in a cloak, with the face of a man that was two hundred years old.

But it was the face of The Great Calosto.

He peered through the bars.

'Young, and fresh!' he croaked. 'Soon, your blood will make me young again!'

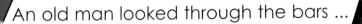

Chapter 4:
The return

The ancient figure shuffled away down the passage. Then a young woman, in an old-fashioned costume, appeared from the direction of the cabinet.

'Where am I?' she screamed. 'What's happened to me?'

'Open the door with the key, quickly,' said Emma. 'We'll escape together!'

The back door of the cabinet was waiting for them. Carefully, Emma opened it. She saw the sword come through, heard the gasp of the audience. The sword was pulled out again.

'Follow me!' Emma said

But there was only room for one person in the box.

There was a roar of amazement, and loud applause.

Emma bowed to the audience and left the stage.

There was something she couldn't understand. The audience had changed. They were wearing strange clothes ...

At the back of the stage she saw a notice, advertising the show.

Don't miss – The Great Calosto!

One night only!

October 31st 1857 ...

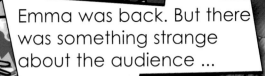

Magic word check

audience

cabinet

code word

compartment

curse

demon

equipment

hag stone

handcuffs

Harry Houdini

magician

mascot

medicine man

mind reading

mummified

shaman

witch

witch bottle

witchcraft

wizard